AKIN'S ADVENTU[RES]
THE RICHEST MAN TO EVER LIVE

Written By:
Arreal Parson

GENERATIONAL PRESS
Richmond, Virginia

Hardcover ISBN: 978-1-7377822-2-3
Paperback ISBN: 978-1-7377822-0-9
E-book ISBN: 978-1-7377822-1-6
Audio Book ISBN: 978-1-7377822-3-0
Library of Congress Control Number (LCCN): 2021917103

Written by: Arreal Parson
Edited by: Starr Balmer-Chore
Illustrated by: Arsalan
Book design by: Arreal Parson

GENERATIONAL PRESS
Richmond, Virginia

Email: info@generationalpress.com
Website: www.generationalpress.com
Facebbok: GENERATIONAL PRESS
Instagram: @generationalpress

Dedication:

This book is dedicated to my younger brother Bryce, and the other adventurous boys and girls who are not afraid to live out their wonderful imaginations.
Always remember, you can become whatever you dream of!

~Arreal Parson~

"Akin! Akin! Do you hear me talking to you?"
Akin's mother asked.
Akin sat on his bed staring out his window.
"Uh, uh yes ma'am," Akin replied.
"I want you to clean up this room before your dad gets home from work."
"Yes ma'am."

Akin hopped off his bed and began to pick up all the toys, clothes, and games that covered his bedroom floor. The sun was shining brightly through Akin's bedroom window. Akin began to drift back into his imagination as the sun rays hit his face.

Akin traveled all the way back to the 14th century.

"I'm Mansa Musa, King of Mali," Akin proclaimed.

Mansa Musa was a West African king who ruled over the Malian Empire. He is known to be the richest man to ever live.
Akin imagined himself sitting on a camel, wearing an expensive robe, adorned in the finest of gold.

"Yes, everyone, I am Mansa Musa, and I come with gifts! I have gifts for everyone!"

As Mansa Musa traveled throughout the world, he shared his wealth. He gave gold and other fine gifts to the poor.

Mansa Musa not only gave gifts and gold to the poor, but also shared his knowledge with them.

"I come to share what I've learned," Akin said as he stood on his chair imagining himself teaching a crowd of people in the city of Timbuktu.

Mansa Musa built mosques, monuments, and universities throughout his land and other lands he traveled to. One notable university was The University of Sankore.

Akin began grabbing his toy blocks and started stacking them on top of each other.

"I've constructed these beautiful buildings so you all can have great places to come together and learn," Akin said as he continued to stack his toy blocks HIGHER and HIGHER and HIGHER until his mother walked in to check on his progress.

"Akin, Akin! Look at this room!" His mother yelled.
Akin jumped up and bumped into the tower of toy blocks.

Akin stood there looking around at the disaster in his room.

"Why are you wrapped in your blanket?" His mother asked.

"It's my pretend robe, I was Mansa Musa and..."

Before Akin could finish his mother interrupted him. "Akin, how do you know about Mansa Musa?"

"Well, when I was cleaning my room, the sun hit my face and I became Mansa Musa, King of Mali," Akin replied.

"Akin, you have one great imagination. Now, let me help you clean this room before your dad gets home," his mother said. Akin smiled as he and his mother began to clean his room.

"Mother, can I tell you all about Mansa Musa?" Akin asked with great enthusiasm. "Sure, as long as you continue to clean this room," his mother replied.
Akin continued to clean as he told his mother all about his adventures as Mansa Musa, King of Mali.

As Akin and his mother finished putting away his toys, the bedroom door opened. CREAK! CREAK! The door squeaked. "Dad, you're home!" Akin ran to his dad and gave him a great big hug.

"Hey there, my little king," Akin's dad said. Akin's mother smiled as she watched their embrace.

"Yes, Dad, I am a king."
"I'm Mansa Musa!" Akin shouted.
"Who is Mansa Musa?" Akin's dad asked.
"He was the King of Mali," Akin said.

"Oh, your son has one great big imagination," Akin's mother said.
"Akin, tell your dad all about your adventure as Mansa Musa."
Akin smiled and began to tell his dad all about Mansa Musa, The Richest Man to Ever Live!

10 Fun Facts About Mansa Musa

1. Mansa Musa's exact date of birth is unknown, but it is believed he was born around the year 1280.

2. Mansa Musa is believed to be the richest man in history with an estimated net worth of over $400 billion.

3. Mansa Musa is believed to be either the grandson or grandnephew of Sundiata Keita (founder of the Empire of Mali).

4. Mansa Musa was the 10th ruler of the Empire of Mali.

5. Mansa Musa ruled the Empire of Mali for 25 years. The approximate date for Mansa Musa's rule is 1307-1332.

6. In 1324, the 17th year of his rule, Mansa Musa took a pilgrimage to Mecca, which became legendary due to the extreme wealth he displayed throughout his journey.

7. Mansa Musa's extreme generosity of gold giving caused economic upset in the cities he traveled to. Due to the overabundance of gold, its value declined, which caused inflation in those cities.

8. In 1327, Mansa Musa built the Great Mosque at Timbuktu.

9. Timbuktu became famous worldwide as a major cultural and trade city during Mansa Musa's rule.

10. Mansa Musa's son Mansa Maghan succeeded his father and ruled the Empire of Mali from 1337 to 1341.

Mansa Musa

Map of Ancient Empire of Mali

The map highlights in yelllow text the major cities that were a part of the Mali Empire. Also, the map includes the countries that bordered the Mali Empire.

*The information provided in this book is a guide to learning about the great Mansa Musa and the Mali Empire. It is encouraged to do further research with your child/student to learn more about the history of The Richest Man to Ever Live!

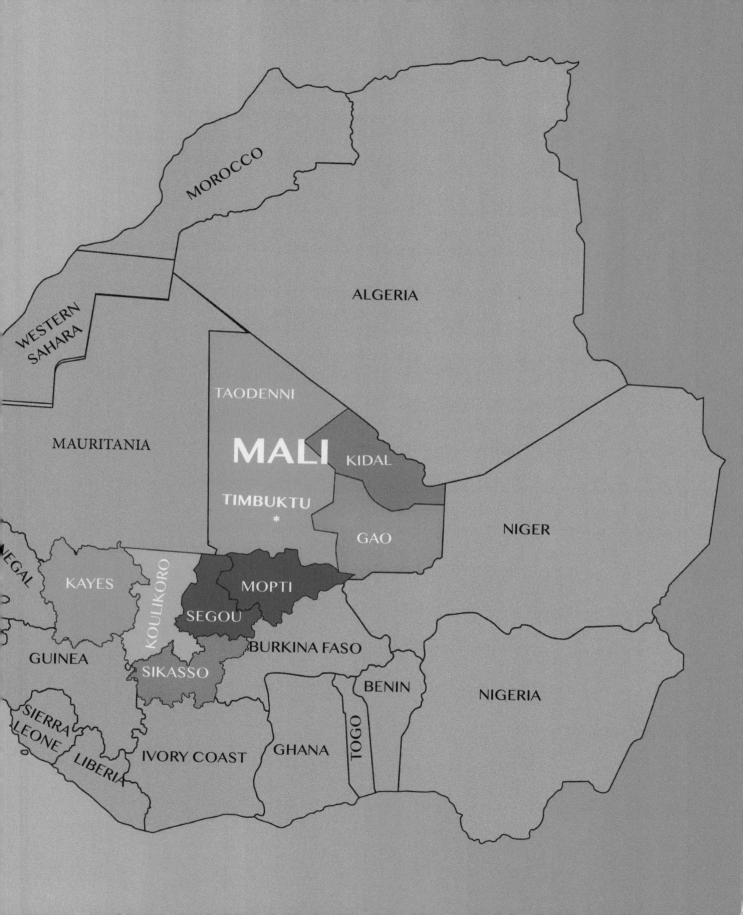

About the Author

Arreal Parson was born in Richmond, Virginia, a city located in the southeast region of the United States. This is the place where Parson's interest in creative writing all started.

Throughout childhood, Parson found writing to be her refuge. Writing helped her to express her self in ways she dreaded verbally. Growing up, she indulged in writing poetry, songs, books, and other forms of creative writing.

Arreal Parson graduated from Norfolk State University (NSU) with honors. She received a bachelor's degree in psychology, with a focus on child psychology. While at NSU, Parson was inducted into the Psi Chi National Honors Society in Psychology. Her studies at NSU helped shape her writing style to reflect the audience she caters to.

Parson's mission is to write children's books that inspire self-love, integrity, acceptance, learning, curiosity, and adventure within her young readers. She is currently working on two different book series, "Akin's Adventures" and "Queenie" to help accomplish her goals.

CPSIA information can be obtained
at www.ICGtesting.com
Printed in the USA
BVHW020746060422
633360BV00007B/70

9 781737 782209